my first Maths BOOK

ARCTURUS

ARCTURUS

This edition published in 2019 by Arcturus Publishing Limited
26/27 Bickels Yard, 151–153 Bermondsey Street,
London SE1 3HA

Illustrator: Amanda Enright
Designer: Trudi Webb
Cover designer: Ms Mousepenny
Writer: Paul Virr

ISBN: 978-1-78950-312-8
CH007274NT
Supplier 33, Date 0519, Print run 8581

Printed in China

How to use this book

Here are some helpful hints to help you solve the puzzles.

Read the questions carefully to work out what you are being asked to do.

Always count slowly and steadily. Don't rush!

Check your answers at the back of the book, to make sure that you got everything right!

Parent's note:

This book is intended to support the learning your child does at school. You can help by encouraging your child to try all of the puzzles, even the ones they think may be difficult. Have a notebook handy so your child can write down their answers, or you may prefer to write directly into the book. Remember to have fun!

Counting Sheep

Little Bo Peep is counting her sheep! How many black sheep are there? How many white sheep? And how many sheep are there altogether?

Sharing Snacks

These children like to share. Can you give each child the same number of strawberries?

CHILLY CHALLENGE

Help this little penguin to get home as fast as she can. She can only step on the triangle-shaped icebergs!

Triangles have 3 sides.

START

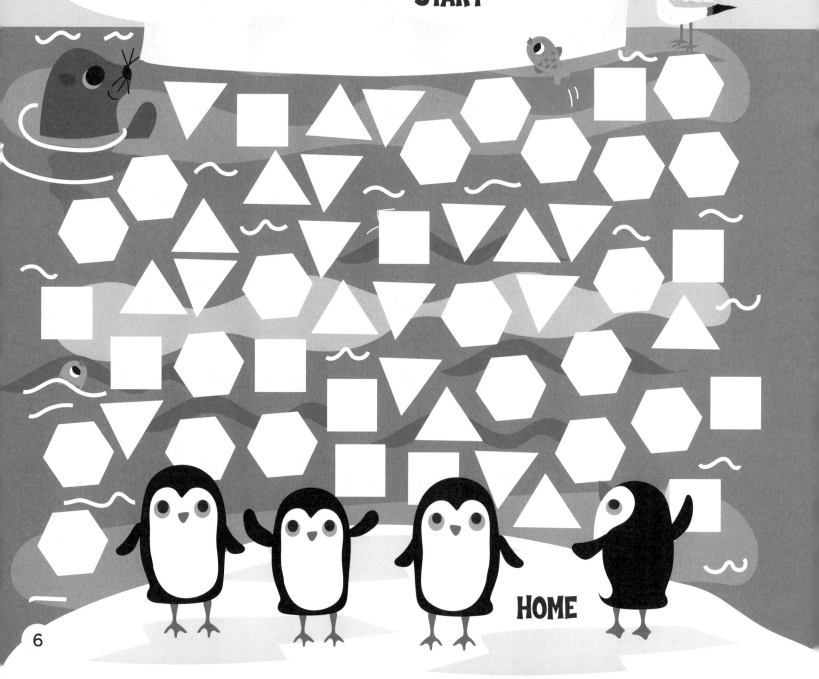

HOME

6

Pizza Puzzle

Everyone's ordering pizza! Help the waiter work out how many slices to give each hungry customer.

Gone Fishing

Who has caught the most fish, the red team or the blue team? How many more fish did they catch than the losing team?

Happy Hens

Each happy hen lays eggs that match its feathers. Which hen has laid the most? How many eggs will the farmer collect?

Wacky Wheels

Everyone is whizzing about! How many wheels can you count? How many wheels would be left if all the scooters zoomed off home?

Spot Spotting

How many groups of bugs with the same number of spots can you find? Get out your magnifying glass, and take a closer look!

CIRCUS SHOW

Let's go to the circus! Which juggler is juggling numbers that add up to nine?

Apple Picking

Help the farmer to pick her apples.
How many red apples are there?
Are there more green apples or red apples?

Flower Finder

Just look at all these pretty flowers! How many flowers can you find that have six petals?

Cupcakes to Go!

Time for a tasty treat! If each child makes a different choice, which plate will have three treats left?

a

b

c

d

Windy Day Fun

It's windy today—let's fly some kites! How many triangles can you see within each kite? It's more than four!

Triangles have three sides!

ON SAFARI

Can you spot three groups of three zebras? How many zebras is that?

There are four groups of two elephants. How many elephants can you spot?

Robot Factory

These shiny robots are ready to work together! Can you spot the robots that show an even number?

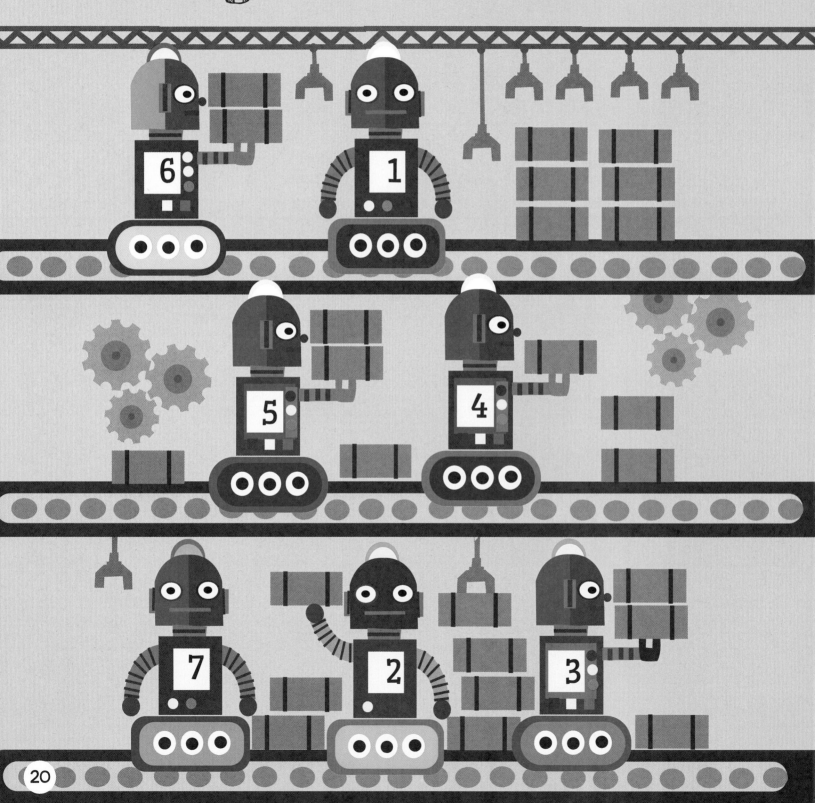

Frog Hopper

If every frog hops three lily pads down the page, which frog will land on lily pad number 6?

Road Racers

Add the numbers on the runners' tops. The team with the largest number wins the race! Which team will win?

Answers

Page 4 Counting Sheep

There are 4 black sheep, and 3 white sheep.
There are 7 sheep altogether.

Page 5 Sharing Snacks

Each child should have 3 strawberries.

Page 6 Chilly Challenge

Page 7 Pizza Puzzles

The first customer needs 2 slices.
The second customer needs 1 slice.
The third customer needs 4 slices.

Page 8 Gone Fishing

The red team has caught 11 fish, and the blue team has caught 7 fish. The red team has caught 4 more fish than the blue team.

Page 9 Happy Hens

The brown hen has laid 9 eggs, which is the most. The farmer will collect 21 eggs.

Page 10 Wacky Wheels

There are 18 wheels in the picture. There would be 8 wheels left if the scooters zoomed home.

Page 11 Spot Spotting

There are 4 groups of bugs.

Page 12 Circus Show

Juggler b.

Page 13 Apple Picking

There are 10 red apples. There are more green apples than red apples.

Pages 14-15 Flower Finder

There are 6 flowers with 6 petals.

Page 16 Cupcakes to Go

Plate b.

Page 17 Windy Day Fun

There are 8 triangles within each kite.

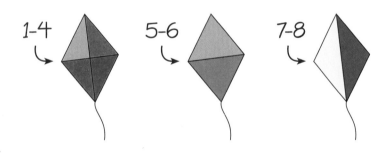

1-4   5-6   7-8

Pages 18-19 On Safari

There are 3 groups of 3 zebras, which is 9 zebras altogether. There are 8 elephants.

Page 20 Robot Factory

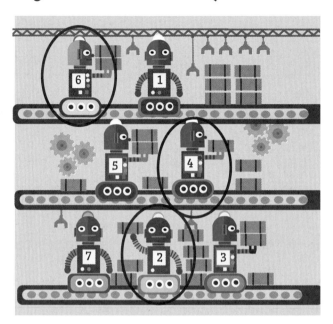

Page 21 Frog Hopper

Frog d.

Page 22 Road Racers

Red team = 14 points.
Blue team = 12 points.
Yellow team = 15 points.
Green team = 11 points.
The yellow team will win.